Father Christmas Goes on Holiday

Raymond Briggs

PUFFIN

For Jean

PUFFIN BOOKS

UK | USA | Canada | Ireland | Australia | India | New Zealand | South Africa

Puffin Books is part of the Penguin Random House group of companies
whose addresses can be found at global.penguinrandomhouse.com.

www.penguin.co.uk www.puffin.co.uk www.ladybird.co.uk

First published in Great Britain by Hamish Hamilton 1975
Published in the United States of America by Coward, McCann & Geoghegan 1975
Published in Picture Puffins 1977
Published in this edition 2014
004

Printed in China
A CIP catalogue record for this book is available from the British Library

ISBN: 978-0-723-29741-3

All correspondence to:
Puffin Books, Penguin Random House Children's
80 Strand, London WC2R 0RL

Other books by Raymond Briggs

JIM AND THE BEANSTALK
FATHER CHRISTMAS
FUNGUS THE BOGEYMAN
THE SNOWMAN

Father Christmas goes on Holiday

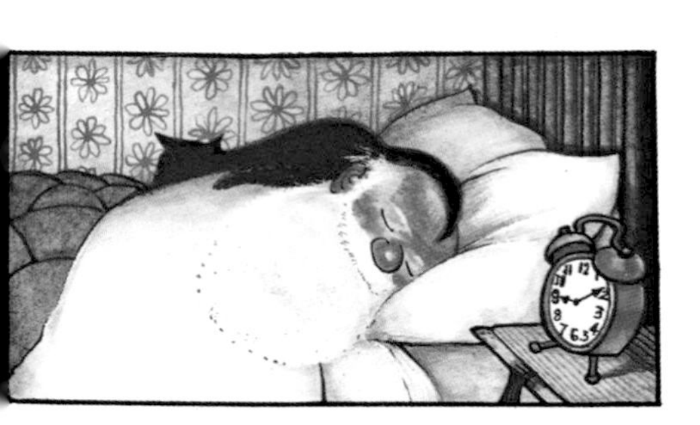

?
ITALIA
GO DUTCH
SPAIN
USA
GB
GRANNY'S COOKIES

LATER
ITALY? AMERICA?
THIS WEEK GARDENER'S QUESTION TIME COMES FROM

GREECE? IRELAND?
PINCH OUT THE TIPS

ENGLAND? HOLLAND?
CUT WELL BACK

CANADA? GERMANY?
PLENTY OF GOOD MUCK

FRANCE!

YES! FRANCE! LAND OF CULTURE, ART, CIVILIZATION FOOD! WINE! SUN!

FOOD!

WINE!

SUN!

FOOD, WINE, SUN!
THIS WEEK'S TOPICAL TIPS..

BETTER SWOT U
ME FRENCH

JE SUIS,
TU ES,
IL EST,
BILL SOWERBUTTS

WHERE TO STAY?

DON'T LIKE FANCY HOTELS MUCH

YES! CAMPING! THE SIMPLE LIFE!

NO! NOT TENTS!

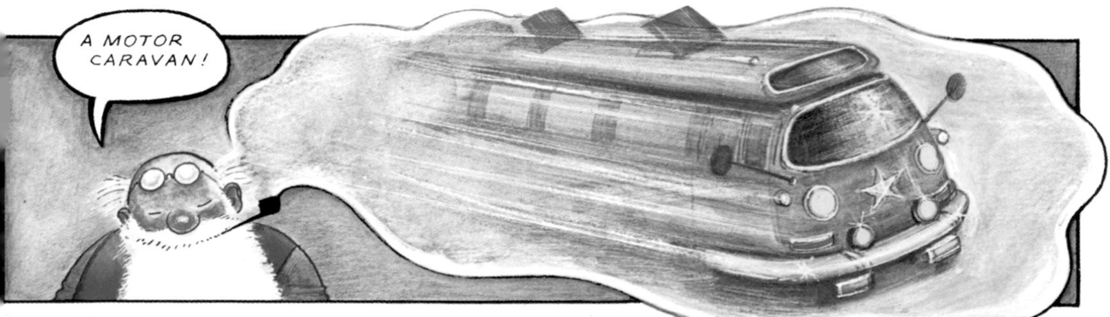
A MOTOR CARAVAN!

TOO EXPENSIVE

IDEA!

MAKE THE SLEDGE INTO A CARAVAN! THEN I CAN FLY!

SERVICE FRANÇAIS DE LA BBC
PLANS

JE SUIS, TU ES,

LA PLUME DE MA TANTE, LESSON NUMBER THREE

UN, DEUX, TROIS,

LA PLUME DE MA TANTE, LESSON NUMBER SIX
I COULD TELL YOU WHAT TO DO WITH THE PLUME OF YOUR BLOOMING TANTE, MATE

ICI PARIS

TRÈS BON!
WET PAINT Keep off cat
PLANS
SOCKS, VESTS PANTS, SHIRTS, TROUSERS, JACKET, HATS....
TEA, SUGAR, CORNFLAKES, MARGE, KETCHUP, JAM, BAKED BEANS....
FLIPPER FEET, CAMERA, EASEL, TORCH BINOCULARS, BIRD BOOK
NORTHERN KENNELS INC
GOODBYE CAT
GOODBYE DOG

LA BELLE FRANCE!

-ER, BONJOUR, MADEMOISELLE
MADAME! S'IL VOUS PLAIT! BONJOUR, M'SIEUR

OH - ER, PARDON, **MADAME** - ER - JE VEUX ACHETER LE LAIT, S'IL VOUS PLAIT

DU LAIT? OUI, M'SIEUR

MERCI, MADAME!
MERCI, M'SIEUR!

I SPOKE FRENCH! I SPOKE FRENCH!

THIS IS THE LIFE!

WHAT'S THAT?

BLOOMING MARVELLOUS!

GOLDEN ORIOLE! NEVER SEEN ONE BEFORE. ONE MORE TO TICK OFF

BETTER GO SHOPPING IN A MINUTE

BLOOMING FUNNY BREAD

WISH I DIDN'T LOOK SO LIKE A BLOOMING FOREIGNER

AH!

BLEU DE TRAVAI
MAGNIFIQUE, M'SIEUR!

THAT'S BETTER- LOOK MORE FRENCH, NOW

NOT SO CONSPICUOUS

UN TABLE POUR UN PERSONNE, S'IL VOUS PLAIT
OUI, M'SIEUR

I EXPECT HE THINKS I'M FRENCH
RESTAU

L'APERITIF M'SIEUR
MERCI, ME OLD MATE. I'M GOING TO HAVE A BASH AT EVERYTHING GOING
Menu
Restaurant Normande

ESCARGOTS
À LA CRÈME
SNAILS IN CRE
GOLLY!
FOOD IN FRANCE

LE VIN M'SIEUR
MERCI, OLD SON, SLOSH IT OUT

HOMARD À LA CRÈME - LOBSTER IN CREAM! LUSCIOUS!
FOOD IN FRANCE

ROGNONS DE VEAU À LA CRÈME - VEAL KIDNEYS IN CREAM!

LOVELY WINE!

NO CHIPS, MATE?
POMMES SAUTÉES, M'SIEUR

NO BLOOMING CHIPS!

ANY ETCHUP?
NON, M'SIEUR!

HP SAUCE?
NON! M'SIEUR

DADDY'S FAVOURITE SAUCE?
NON! MONSIEUR!

NO BLOOMING SAUCE! WHAT A COUNTRY!

CRÈME À L'ORANGE! DON'T HAVE TO LOOK THAT UP!

CAFÉ CRÈME COGNAC, M'SIEUR

!
CRUMBS! BLOOMING EXPENSIVE!
Restaurant Normande

?

M'SIEUR! SERVICE NON COMPRIS!

OH SORRY, GARCON MATE HERE YOU ARE OLD SON, AND THE BEST OF LUCK!

THAT AFTERNOON
BLOOMING MARVELLOUS LIGHT!
OH DEAR! FEEL A BIT QUEER IN THE TUM
OH DEAR!
WHERE'S THE ALKA-WHATSIT?
WHERE'S THAT DIO-STUFF?
OOOH, DEAR!
BLOOMING FLIES!
LIGHT A FIRE-THAT WILL FIX 'EM
OH, FOR A CHIMNEY!

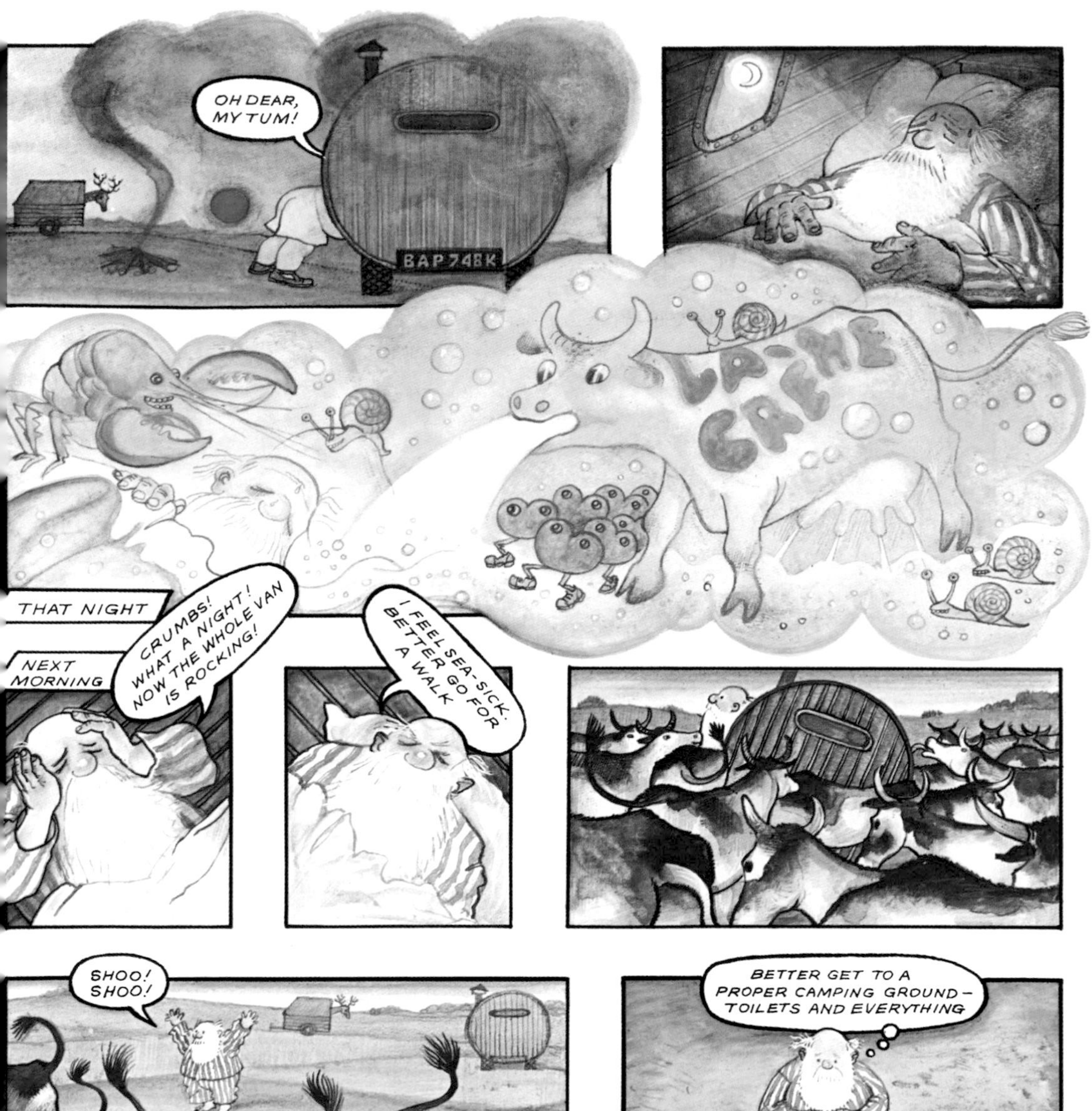
OH DEAR, MY TUM!
BAP 748K
THAT NIGHT
NEXT MORNING
CRUMBS! WHAT A NIGHT! NOW THE WHOLE VAN IS ROCKING!
I FEEL SEA-SICK. BETTER GO FOR A WALK

SHOO! SHOO!

BETTER GET TO A PROPER CAMPING GROUND – TOILETS AND EVERYTHING

CRUMBS!

HOMMES
OH DEAR!

NEXT MORNING
J.V.L.
CRUMBS!

BLOOMING DIARRHOEA!
HOMMES

IT'S ALL THIS FANCY FRENCH FOOD – OR THE DRAINS

A GOOD SOLID BREAKFAST WILL SETTLE THE OLD TUM

ER– LE PETIT DÉJEUNER, S'IL VOUS PLAIT
OUI M'SIEUR

!
VOILA M'SIEUR!

LOOK, OLD SON, JE VEUX LES OEUFS ET BACON AVEC LES CORNFLAKES ET LE TOAST ET MARMALADE, MATE. COMPRENEZ?

ET UN GRAND POT DE THÉ, AUSSI!

IMPOSSIBLE! M'SIEUR, IMPOSSIBLE!

CALL THAT A BREAKFAST?
MON DIEU! MON DIEU!

REGARD, MAMAN!
C'EST PÈRE NOËL!
OH, VIENS VITE!
TIME TO BE MOVING ON

OH CRUMBS! THAT'S DONE IT!

THAT EVENING
HERE, YOU KNOW THAT BLOKE WHO LOOKS LIKE FATHER CHRISTMAS?
YES, WHAT ABOUT HIM?

HE'S GOT TWO REINDEER WITH HIM
OH, GET AWAY!
DEFINITELY TIME TO BE MOVING ON

MUST GET OUT OF HERE
GUIDE to the WORLD

FIND SOMEWHERE MORE HYGIENIC- BETTER DRAINS
ATLA

NO DIARRHOEA- PURER WATER
GUIDE
MA

PURE WATER.... **SCOTLAND!** OF COURSE!

THE BEST WATER IN THE WORLD! AFTER ALL THEY MAKE WHISKY WITH IT!

NEXT DAY
CRUMBS! WHAT A PLACE!

WELL, AT LEAST THERE'S PLENTY OF PURE WATER

WHAT'S THAT?

HERON! BLOOMING MARVELLOUS!

BETTER GET THE SHOPPING
JOLLY COLD!

GOOD MORNING
AAAARGH!

BLOOMING MARVELLOUS!

I'M FAIR DRY, SIR!
BAR

CHEERS!
CHEERS!

CHEERS!

ANGUS McNABB KILTS

HAMISH McHAMILTON
HAGGIS
MUST TRY ONE!

HEY MAM! DID YE NO SEE THAT BIG MAN? IT'S FEYTHER CHRISTMAS!
OCH, AWA WI' YE!
TIME TO BE MOVING ON ALREADY?

THAT EVENING
HAGGIS, SWEDE AND WHISKY! LOVELY!

NEXT MORNING
CRUMBS! IT'S NOT RAINING!
THE SUN! HOORAY!
YIPPEE!
AAAARGH!
IT'S FREEZING
I CAN'T I CAN'T
CRUMBS!
HELP!
SHARKS

QUICK! LOCK THE DOOR!

RAIN ~ COLD SHARKS! WHAT A COUNTRY!

BETTER GET OUT OF HERE TOO WET, TOO COLD

OOOH! LOVELY HOT TEA!

NO GOOD BEING CLEAN IF IT'S COLD

PLENTY OF BLOOMING COLD AT HOME!

WHERE'S SOMEWHERE REALLY HOT? REALLY DRY?
ATLAS

DESERT?

SAHARA? NOTHING THERE –NEVADA?

OF COURSE! LAS VEGAS!

THE FOLLOWING EVENING
NEROS PALACE
HM, NOT BAD LITTLE HOTEL

NEROS
PALACE
THE GLORY OF NOW
LAS VEGAS
NEVADA

HM, NICE LITTLE ROOM
IN NEROS NOSHORIUM
HM, NOT BAD LITTLE SNACKS
MORE FRENCH FRIES, SIR?
KETCHUP, SIR?
NEROS KETCHUP
QUITE GOOD LITTLE PUDDINGS, TOO
BETTER POSH MESELF UP FOR THE EVENING
WHERE'S THAT MONOCLE OUT OF THE CHRISTMAS CRACKER?
AH!

IN NERO'S CASINO

LATER
CRUMBS! RUNNING OUT OF MONEY ALREADY!
OH DEAR, KEEP DOZING OFF..... GETTING OLD..... BEDTIME.......

NEXT MORNING
NICE SUNNY DAY! MUST HAVE A SWIM!
HOPE IT'S NOT TOO COLD!
BLOOMING MARVELLOUS! LIKE AN OVEN!
CRUMBS! 120 DEGREES!
BLISS!
THIS IS THE LIFE!

TA, DUCKS
LAS VEGAS
SUN TAN
The Facts of BLACK JACK
SO THE LAZY DAYS AND WICKED NIGHTS FLY BY, UNTIL........

HEY MOM! IS THAT FAT GUY SANTA CLAUS?
AW, C'MON HERBIE!
TIME TO BE OFF AGAIN
NEROS CASHORIVM
CRUMBS! RUNNING LOW ON MONEY!
HEY MAC! ARE YOU SANTA CLAUS?
BETTER SEE ABOUT THE DEERS AND GET THE BILL
WELL SIR, THEY'VE EATEN 64 BAGS OF POTATO CHIPS, 28 BAGS OF POPCORN, 19 GIANT-SIZE TINS OF PEANUTS AND 26 PACKETS OF SUGAR FROSTIES!
NEROS GARAGES
HERE YOU ARE OLD SON, AND THE BEST OF LUCK!
!!!
I'D CERTAINLY **BETTER** GO HOME!
NEROS CHECK
CHEERIO, NERO, ME OLD MATE! THANKS FOR A NICE TIME

HOME WE GO DEERS!

NEXT MORNING
HOORAY! HOME AGAIN!

GARDEN'S GROWN! BLOOMING WEEDS!

THANK HEAVEN THAT'S OVER

BETTER GET THE CAT AND DOG

HULLO CAT! HULLO DOG!

THERE'S THE BLOOMING POST ALREADY

GETS EARLIER EVERY BLOOMING YEAR

BETTER GET DOWN TO IT IN A MINUTE

GET ME TUM BACK TO NORMAL

BETTER PUT THE OLD RED WORK CLOTHES ON AGAIN

NOT THAT THERE'S ANYONE HERE TO SEE

STUCK UP HERE

ON ME OWN

IN THE COLD

STILL, AT LEAST I'VE HAD A BLOOMING GOOD HOLIDAY!